Christmas
Doodles

illustrated by Non Figg

Edited by Phil Clarke

Add more branches to the snowy trees.

Turn these blobs into snowmen
with hats and scarves.

Draw plenty of gifts beneath the tree.

Doodle patterns on the decorations.

Fill in the gift tag, and add decorations.

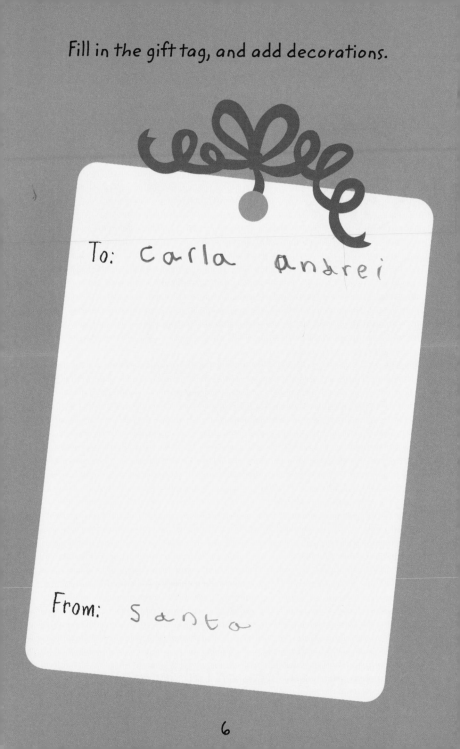

To: carla   andrei

From: santa

Draw more penguins on the ice.

Draw matching designs on the hat and scarf.

Decorate these Christmas cupcakes.

Draw what the pets might want for Christmas.

Give Rudolph more antlers.

Add holly, flowers and ribbons to this wreath.

Doodle more sheep in the snowy field.

Add birds to the wintry branches.

Serve up some Christmas party food for these hungry bears.

Doodle roofs and chimneys on the houses.

Fill the stocking with lots of presents.

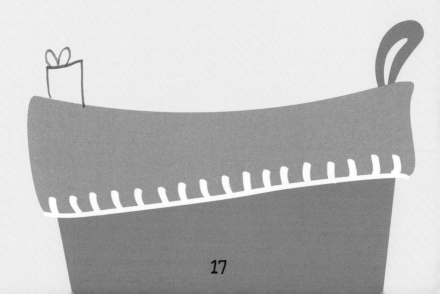

Dress up this gingerbread man.

Decorate Santa's sleigh and fill it with presents.

Draw a bird on the holly branch.

Give each snowman a different look.

Draw a cat on the windowsill, watching the snow fall.

Finish the double tracks in the snow, swerving between the trees.

23

Draw a baby penguin between its father's feet.

Add lots of lights and decorations to the Christmas tree.

Give the dog a Santa hat.

Draw the other half of the snowflake.
Try to match the patterns exactly.

Draw the snowballs the children are throwing.

Draw ducks with scarves on the frozen pond.

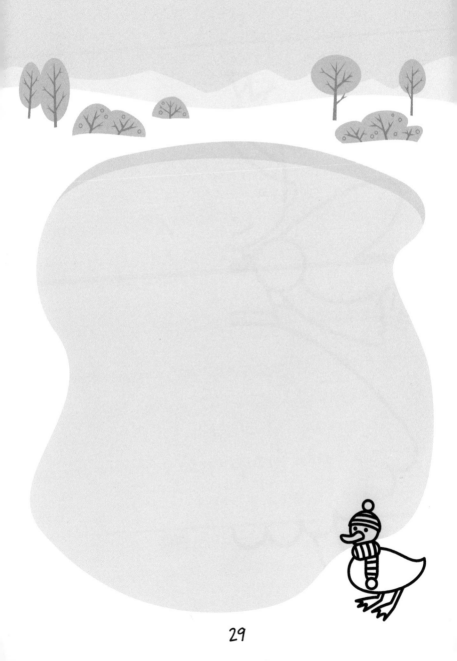

Draw the other half of the fairy.

Add a door and lots of windows to
the Snow Queen's ice palace.

Draw some food for Santa and his reindeer, and leave him a message.

Dear Santa,

love from,

Fill the street with Christmas lights.

Draw this mother polar bear's little cubs.

Draw a head, hands and feet on the Christmas
tree angel, and decorate her dress.

Doodle or write the things you
would like for Christmas.

Dear Santa,

I would like... a soft

Toy

...please.

Thank you very much.
Love, from carla

Draw a line as fast as you can from the children to the snowman without sliding off the trail.

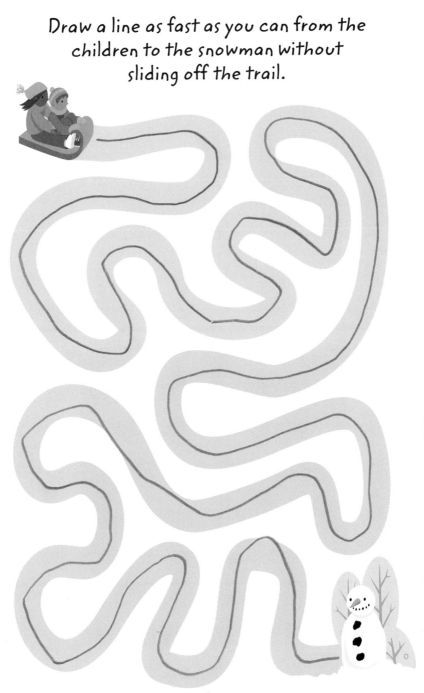

Draw Santa's boots sticking out of the chimney.

Decorate the gingerbread house with
lollipops and candy canes.

Give the dog a warm hat, scarf and coat.

Draw the other half of the penguin, then add snowflakes.

Show all the tracks the reindeer and
rabbit have made in the snow.

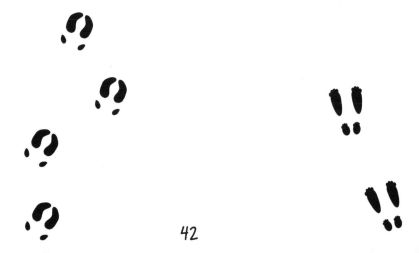

Build a house where Santa would feel at home.

Give the carol singers hats and scarves.

Decorate the presents with ribbons, bows and tags.

Draw a line to lead the bunny to its winter carrot supply.

Doodle fir trees in the snow.

Design your own Christmas cards.

Decorate these Christmas cookies with lines, spots and swirls.

Draw a snowman in the globe.
Add snowflakes around him.

Hang more Christmas stockings over the fireplace.

Give the Snow Queen a frosty expression.

Draw decorations on the branches.

Draw the other half of Rudolph's head.

Design your own star by joining the dots.

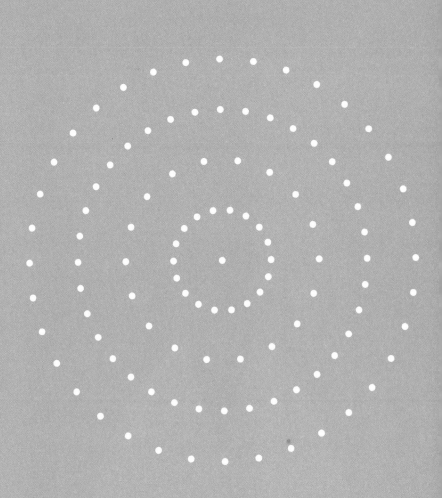

Draw a Santa hat on the penguin.

Decorate the garlands.

Show the toys the elves have made.

Add stripes or spots to the hat and scarf.

This Christmas angel needs some wings.

Doodle patterns on the candy canes.

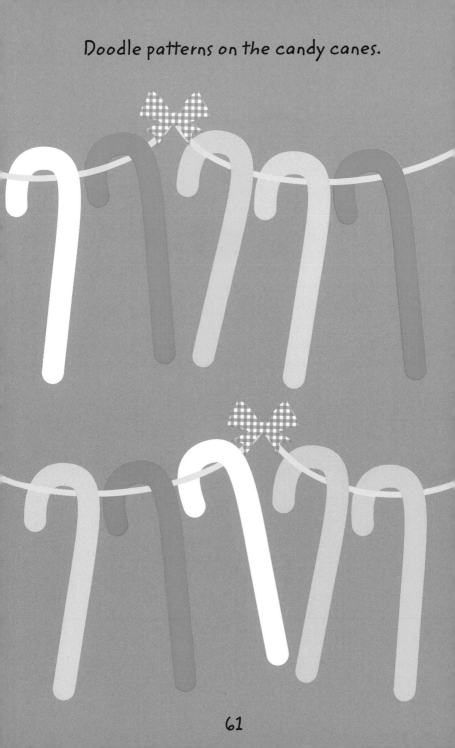

Fill the icy sea with fish.

Fill the sky with snowflakes.

Complete the Christmas card.

Hang lots of bells on the tree.

Add wings to the Christmas fairies.

Give the penguins balloons and party hats.

Use the lines to design your own snowflake.

Design a Christmas stamp.

What has the polar bear caught
on his fishing line?

Fill the branches with tasty treats.

Decorate the crowns with patterns and jewels.

○ ○ ◇ ○ ○

Draw a line as fast as you can from the signpost to Santa's sleigh without leaving the trail.

North Pole

Draw ski tracks in the snow.

Fill in the dotted shapes to see what's hiding in the picture.

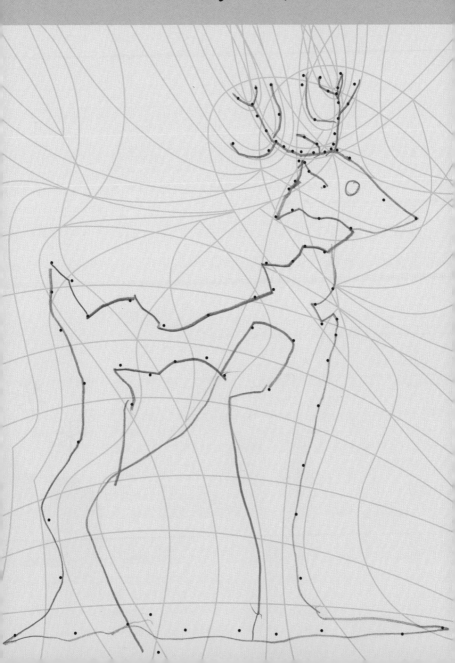

Draw lots more berries on the mistletoe.

Decorate the stocking and fill it with presents.

What gift have you just unwrapped?

Decorate the door with a wreath and Christmas lights.

Continue the patterns onto the other side of the present.

Design an outfit for a Christmas party.

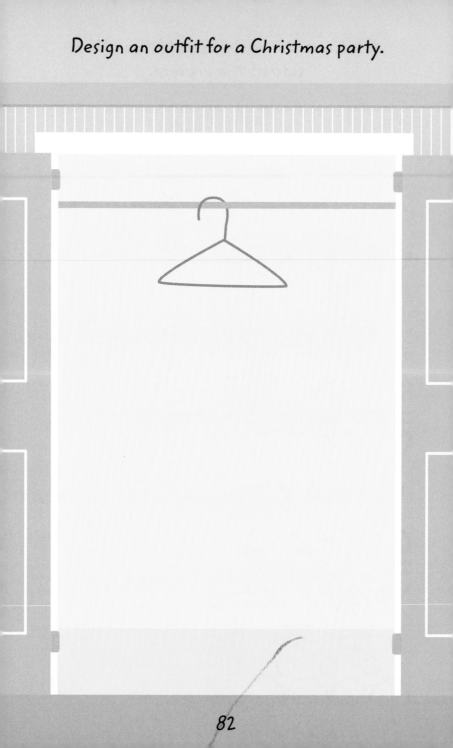

Finish the elf's face and give him a hat.

Trace all the lines in each decoration
without lifting your pen or going
along the same line twice.

Doodle patterns on the wrapping paper.

Draw a Christmas tree in the red pot, then decorate it.

Santa needs some boots and a belt
with a big buckle.

Draw a Christmas design on the mug.

Make sure every face has a party mask.

Doodle stars and snowflakes, and decorate
the house, inside and out.

90

Add details to all the owls.

Doodle patterns on the stockings.

Draw more toys in this Christmas window display.

Fill the sleighs with elves.

Doodle patterns on the gloves.

Hang a bell on every ribbon.

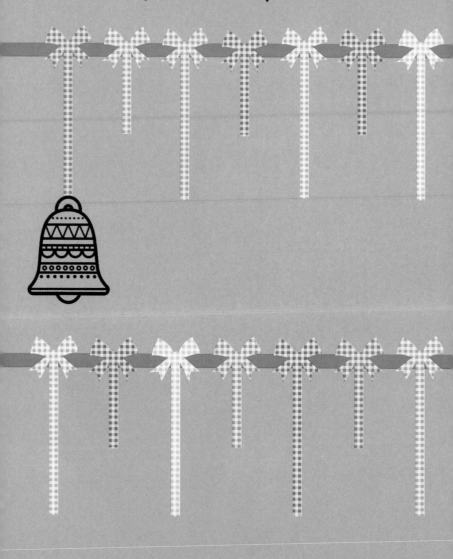

Add ice skates, and give each skater a face.

Draw in Santa's face and beard.

Give the snowman a face, hat, arms
and some buttons.

Doodle Christmas patterns on the sweater.

Make each Christmas light bulb a different shape.

Finish decorating the advent calendar.

Decorate the dogs' sweaters with Christmassy designs.

Decorate these goodies with wrappers and bows.

What are you dreaming that Santa will bring?

Decide what to put on top of your tree:
a star, a fairy, or something else?

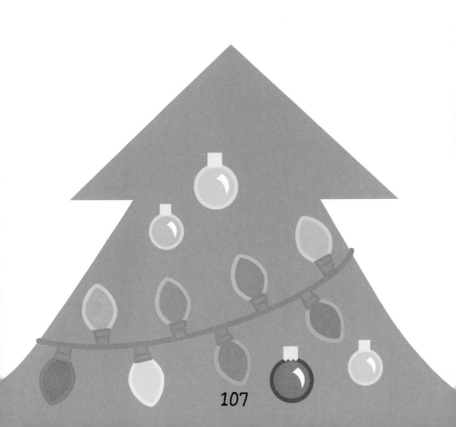

Finish making all the toys.

Give every reindeer a pair of antlers.

Complete the houses with roofs, chimneys, windows and doors.

Draw a line as fast as you can from Santa to the chimney without leaving the trail.

What's for sale at the Christmas market?

Additional designs and illustrations by Sharon Cooper

First published in 2016 by Usborne Publishing Ltd, 83–85 Saffron Hill, London ECIN 8RT, England.
Copyright © 2016 Usborne Publishing Ltd. The name Usborne and the devices ♀♔ are Trade Marks of Usborne Publishing Ltd.